Classics
Volume Nineteen

MY NINETEENTH CLASSIC COLLECTION
CONTAINS:

WAN2TLK?

GET SERIOUS

WHAT'S NOT TO LIKE?

JiM DAViS

ℛℛ

First published by Ravette Publishing 2008.

Printed and bound in Great Britain
for Ravette Publishing Limited,
Unit 3, Tristar Centre,
Star Road, Partridge Green,
West Sussex RH13 8RA

ISBN: 978-1-84161-303-1

GARFIELD
Wan2t1k?

JIM DAVIS   RR

JIM DAVIS 10-12

STAY IN CHARACTER, GARFIELD

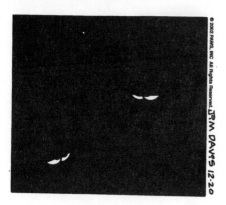

HOW'S THAT HERBAL TEA?

IT'S NOT COFFEE, THAT'S HOW IT IS!

JIM DAVIS 2-3

GARFIELD

Get Serious

JIM DAVIS

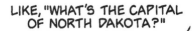

GARFIELD

What's Not to Like?

JIM DAVIS

ℛℛ

RUB RUB
RUB RUB RUB

THAT WAS VERY AFFECTIONATE, GARFIELD

I HAD PEANUT BUTTER ON MY HANDS

JPM DAVIS 8-13

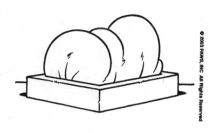

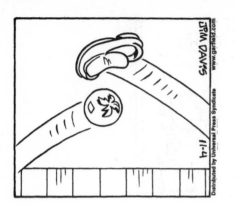

OTHER GARFIELD BOOKS AVAILABLE

Pocket Books		**Price**	**ISBN**
Am I Bothered?		£3.99	978-1-84161-286-7
Compute This!		£3.50	978-1-84161-194-5
Don't Ask!		£3.99	978-1-84161-247-8
Feed Me!		£3.99	978-1-84161-242-3
Get Serious		£3.99	978-1-84161-265-2
Gotcha!		£3.50	978-1-84161-226-3
I Am What I Am!		£3.99	978-1-84161-243-0
I Don't Do Perky		£3.99	978-1-84161-195-2
Kowabunga		£3.99	978-1-84161-246-1
Numero Uno	(new)	£3.99	978-1-84161-297-3
Pop Star		£3.50	978-1-84161-151-8
S.W.A.L.K.		£3.50	978-1-84161-225-6
Time to Delegate	(new)	£3.99	978-1-84161-296-6
Wan2tlk?		£3.99	978-1-84161-264-5
What's Not to Like?		£3.99	978-1-84161-285-0
Theme Books			
Creatures Great & Small		£3.99	978-1-85304-998-9
Entertains You		£4.50	978-1-84161-221-8
Healthy Living		£3.99	978-1-85304-972-9
Pigging Out		£4.50	978-1-85304-893-7
Slam Dunk!		£4.50	978-1-84161-222-5
The Seasons		£3.99	978-1-85304-999-6
2-in-1 Theme Books			
All In Good Taste		£6.99	978-1-84161-209 6
Easy Does It		£6.99	978-1-84161-191 4
Lazy Daze		£6.99	978-1-84161-208 9
Licensed to Thrill		£6.99	978-1-84161-192 1
Out For The Couch		£6.99	978-1-84161-144 0
The Gruesome Twosome		£6.99	978-1-84161-143 3
Classics			
Volume One		£6.99	978-1-85304-970-5
Volume Two		£6.99	978-1-85304-971-2
Volume Three		£6.99	978-1-85304-996-5
Volume Four		£6.99	978-1-85304-997-2
Volume Five		£6.99	978-1-84161-022-1
Volume Six		£6.99	978-1-84161-023-8
Volume Seven		£5.99	978-1-84161-088-7
Volume Eight		£6.99	978-1-84161-089-4
Volume Nine		£6.99	978-1-84161-149-5
Volume Ten		£6.99	978-1-84161-150-1
Volume Eleven		£6.99	978-1-84161-175-4
Volume Twelve		£6.99	978-1-84161-176-1
Volume Thirteen		£6.99	978-1-84161-206-5

Classics (cont'd ...)	**Price**	**ISBN**
Volume Fourteen	£6.99	978-1-84161-207-2
Volume Fifteen	£5.99	978-1-84161-232-4
Volume Sixteen	£5.99	978-1-84161-233-1
Volume Seventeen	£6.99	978-1-84161-250-8
Volume Eighteen	£6.99	978-1-84161-251-5
Volume Twenty (new)	£6.99	978-1-84161-304-8

Gift Books (new series)		
30 Years - The Fun's Just Begun (new)	£9.99	978-1-84161-307-9
Don't Know, Don't Care	£4.99	978-1-84161-279-9
Get a Grip	£4.99	978-1-84161-282-9
I Don't Do Ordinary	£4.99	978-1-84161-281-2
Keep your Attitude, I have my own	£4.99	978-1-84161-278-2

Little Books		
C-c-c-caffeine	£2.50	978-1-84161-183-9
Food 'n' Fitness	£2.50	978-1-84161-145-7
Laughs	£2.50	978-1-84161-146-4
Love 'n' Stuff	£2.50	978-1-84161-147-1
Surf 'n' Sun	£2.50	978-1-84161-186-0
The Office	£2.50	978-1-84161-184-6
Zzzzzz	£2.50	978-1-84161-185-3

Miscellaneous		
Colour Collection Book 2 (new)	£10.99	978-1-84161-306-2
Colour Collection Book 1	£10.99	978-1-84161-293-5
Treasury 7	£10.99	978-1-84161-248-5
Treasury 6	£10.99	978-1-84161-229-4
Treasury 5	£10.99	978-1-84161-198-3
Treasury 4	£10.99	978-1-84161-180-8
Treasury 3	£9.99	978-1-84161-142-6

All Garfield books are available at your local bookshop or from the publisher at the address below.

Just send your order with your payment and name and address details to:-

Ravette Publishing, Unit 3, Tristar Centre, Star Road, Partridge Green, West Sussex RH13 8RA
(tel: 01403 711443 ... email: ravettepub@aol.com)

Prices and availability are subject to change without notice.

Please enclose a cheque or postal order made payable to **Ravette Publishing** to the value of the cover price of the book/s and allow the following for UK postage and packing:-

70p for the first book + 40p for each additional book
except Treasuries & Colour Collections... when please add £3.00 per copy